HOW SOULS ARE MADE

By Roma Chadha Sood

Illustrated by Devika Joglekar

www.howsoulsaremade.com

Printed in the United States of America.

ISBN: 978-0-99696-780-8

from You.

for You.

Deep within the inner sky,

High, high up above,

Lies a very special place,

Called the Land of Love.

Where trees are made of lollipops,

And roses grow ice-creams.

Where chocolate lilies float,

Upon honey-sparkle streams.

Now this land is far different,

From other lands you know.

For here a swan of white and gold,

Could once have been a crow!

The King who rules this magic land,

Is the sweetest king of all.

For when He smiles His magic smile,

Rainbow sparkles start to fall.

Music drips in tinkle notes,

Each one takes his place,

To watch the magic yet again,

From His wand of Grace.

He nods His head and fairies bring,

A little baby child.

No one moves, all watch in awe,

To see what He has styled.

He picks the still child in His arms,

And holds it to His chest.

He raises high the magic wand,

And swirls it east to west.

Enchanting music fills the air,

The child nestled in His hold.

And from His eyes begins to flow,

A shower of shimmering gold.

Golden stardust softly falls,

On lashes resting low.

Breathing life into closed eyes,

Filling cheeks with pinkish glow.

Between the two tiny brows,

He lays His tender hand.

"When you need me, I'm right here,

Your true home is this land.

Give joy and love to all you meet,

For you and I are one.

All I have, I give to you,

Your journey has begun."

The fairies leap, the flowers sing,

The lollipop trees sway.

The swans dance and swoop with joy,

A soul's been made today!

Lashes flutter, a rosebud smile,

A wiggle in its toes.

Tiny fingers grasp His hand,

The first One that it knows.

"You are perfect!" whispers the King,

And He shimmers out of sight.

The baby's eyes flicker open,

Filled with sparkling golden light.

In another world, a mother cries,

She hugs the baby close and tight.

A father stares in silent awe,

At this new and wondrous sight.

This precious gift of joy and love,

Of petal skin and eyes so bright,

Melting hearts of gratitude,

For this babe of golden light.

Years go by and the baby grows,

Through sunshine and through rain.

She laughs, she cries, she walks and plays,

Learning love and pain.

But sometimes she finds that it's dark,

And feels terribly alone.

Like all the warmth of summer is gone,

And she's cold unto the bone.

Unknown longing haunts within,

For something not in sight.

It feels like day will never dawn,

Upon this darkest night.

But deep inside, when she gets still,

She hears a whisper - "I'm right here!"

A gentle presence fills her heart,

And wipes away her every fear.

Filled with wonder she seeks on,

Looking with closed eyes.

While still here, she's reached that land,

Where sun and moon both rise.

Where trees are made of lollipops,

And roses grow ice-creams.

Where chocolate lilies float,

Upon honey-sparkle streams.

The Land of Love - whose King she felt,

Within her, always there.

She only had to turn her gaze,

To be comforted by His care.

So on those days when you feel alone,

Confused or afraid,

Take a time-out from the game,

Remember how souls are made.

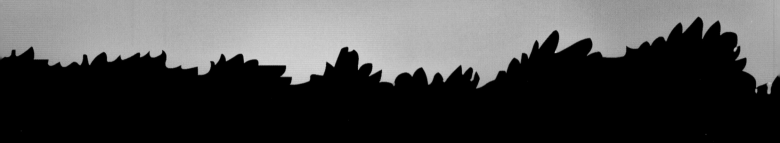

It doesn't matter if you're near a mosque,

A temple or a church,

What matters is your inner connection,

And how intense your search.

A spark was placed inside of you,

By God's own gentle hand.

All that makes you who you are,

Is exactly as He planned.

You are safe. You are loved.

You are His very own.

Never, not for a moment,

Are you ever left alone.

He is your home, your resting place,

You're protected at all times.

His Energy breathes life into you,

Like a gentle breeze through wind chimes.